UNWITTING WISDOM

To Aesop
and all tellers of moral tales who,
despite a monumentally ineffective history,
still gently try to point the human race
in a better direction - h.w.

A TEMPLAR BOOK

First published in 2004 by Templar Publishing.
This edition published in 2023 by Templar Books,
an imprint of Bonnier Books UK
4th Floor, Victoria House,
Bloomsbury Square, London WC1B 4DA
Owned by Bonnier Books
Sveavägen 56, Stockholm, Sweden
www.bonnierbooks.co.uk

ISBN-13: 978-1-800-78620-2

Edited by A. J. Wood
Typography by Mike Jolley

The illustrations in this book are rendered in ink line and watercolour
on uncoated woodfree paper
The text is set in Bernhard Modern BT

Printed in China

# An Anthology of
# AESOP'S
# ANIMAL FABLES

*Unwitting Wisdom*

*Retold & Illustrated*
*by* HELEN WARD

templar
books

One
sour grapes

Two
the trappings of power

Three
all dressed up

Four
pot luck

Five
a time to dance

Six
a dinner invitation

Seven
steady and slow

Eight
upon reflection

Nine
size isn't everything

Ten
not flying, but falling

Eleven
fool's gold

Twelve
hard cheese

# Aesop's fables

So they chose from among themselves some leaders. Charismatic mice who promised victory on the battlefield, mice whose very first act as generals was to order themselves some particularly shiny swords and the very grandest and most exclusive battle helmets with wide, imposing horns. Then, after a very good meal, they sat idly picking their gleaming teeth and passing the port.

The next day the mouse army assembled on the battlefield, with new hope and keenness, to await the advance of the weasels, but when the onslaught came the mice were no more organised than before. As usual the army scattered and fled for the safety of the city. They scuttled through their mouse holes, all except the new generals who were a little too sluggish on their feet and, with the glamorous horns on their gleaming helmets too wide to slip easily through, they were simply captured by the enemy and taken away.

THREE

*all
dressed
up*

IN WHICH A JACKDAW
"BORROWS"
SOME FEATHERS

# THERE WAS ONCE A JACKDAW

who was as black as soot with a bright eye, a voice like a broken bell and some nasty habits that she couldn't help.

She wanted to be a popular and important bird, so she was very careful to be ever so polite and ever so attentive to any bird who had already achieved such status; to cackle loud and long at their bad jokes and compliment their looks, however dull, far, far too often. She was inclined to tread on the sparrows on her way to see the influential eagles and was surprised to find at the end of all her efforts that she was still a very ordinary jackdaw.

One day the jackdaw heard that there was to be a competition to find the most beautiful bird, and she determined that she must win it. Despite being rather plain she had an idea or two behind that glinting eye...

She followed the brighter birds around and collected the feathers that they dropped so carelessly about the place. The sparrows were intrigued but kept their distance, not wanting to lose their own feathers to such an avid collector.

Each evening in her roost the jackdaw cleaned and combed her growing collection. She sorted them by size and colour and threw out those that were too dull or beyond repair. The night before the competition the jackdaw carefully slotted the abandoned feathers in amongst her own. With their stripes and spots, blotches and patches, she settled each in place to create a riotous rainbow of colour, as neat and perfect as if it had grown there of its own accord. She looked quite beautiful in her borrowed feathers. Now it was her turn to shine.

The competitors ruffled up their gorgeous plumes and puffed out their chests. They strutted about and the jackdaw strutted among them, prouder than a peacock, stealing the attention of the judges with a swish of her purloined tail. Who in the audience could resist this sparkling, effervescent bird?

There was no doubt about the winner. The jackdaw was
CERTAINLY THE MOST BEAUTIFUL.

Suddenly, a kerfuffle broke out in the audience. It spread through the crowds and among the competitors. They each began to recognise something familiar in the pattern and the colour of this glamorous bird. They snatched and plucked their feathers back until the deceitful jackdaw was revealed, quite undressed and plain and dull and rather dishevelled. Without her borrowed finery, with no prize for being the most beautiful, no audience to please, no important friends and nothing remarkable to be or to say, she had only herself for company and some hard thinking to be done.

# pot luck

IN WHICH A FOX IS A BAD HOST AND A HUNGRY GUEST

# THERE WAS ONCE A STORK,

a tall and elegant bird, very polite and refined in her habits. She moved to a new neighbourhood and fairly soon received an invitation to dinner. It was from one of the local residents, A FOX.

She knew nothing of the nature of foxes, so when she arrived for dinner she was only a little taken aback to find every course served in shallow dishes. Showing no consideration for his guest the fox lapped his way through the delicious meal with an all too apparent gusto. The stork could only dip the very tip of her beak into the various sauces. She went home more than a little hungry, not to mention offended, while the fox happily finished off the leftovers.

Some weeks later the stork, being a well brought up bird, sent a dinner invitation to the fox. The fox was only too pleased to accept. He liked nothing better than a good meal at someone else's expense.

He did not know that the stork would repay him with a taste of the same consideration that he had shown his own guest.

The stork invited the fox into the dining room. He was tantalised by the wonderful smells wafting through the room. His mouth watered at the prospect of a sumptuous feast, but there was no platter of roasted meats, no dish of gravy or bowl of sauce in the room. Not one morsel of the delicious-smelling food was served in anything other than tall, narrow-mouthed jars, all perfect for the

# LONG BEAK OF A STORK.

Each elegant vessel, fragrant with the promise of food, stopped the fox's snout aggravatingly short of his reach. The stork appeared oblivious to his dilemma. Despite the grandness of the occasion and the polite attentions of the stork, not so much as a buttered pea passed his lips all evening.

The fox went home very hungry and very perplexed. It took him quite a while to work out why he had deserved such treatment. When he finally understood, he felt no better, for he was not at all used to being outsmarted.

SEVEN

*steady and slow*

IN WHICH A HARE IS TOO
CONFIDENT

# THERE WAS ONCE A VERY FAST HARE

AND A VERY SLOW TORTOISE. The hare liked nothing better than impressing the general population with his speed. "I am the master of being faster," was how he so irritatingly put it.

The general population, on the other hand, liked nothing better than discussing the small size of the hare's brain, and where he kept it while he was hurtling about, and how long it would take a crocodile to eat him if he accidentally ran into the river, and whether or not anyone would try to rescue him. Most admitted to a profound respect for the crocodile's teeth but none for any part of the hare.

The tortoise suffered from the hare more than most. The hare humiliated him at every opportunity, but the tortoise was just too gentle and too slow to retaliate.

Before he could say or do anything, the hare was long gone. So the tortoise decided to challenge the hare to a race. The general population thought this was unusually stupid of the tortoise. The hare thought only how certain he was to win. But the tortoise knew what he was doing, the hare being so very predictable.

The race began and the hare hurtled off into the distance. The tortoise plodded forward, settling his thoughts on higher things. Even when the hare hurtled back and ran a few rings around him, the tortoise felt no need to change his even, patient pace.

With so little to challenge his supremacy, the hare decided to take a short nap. The nap turned into a bit of a doze, the doze into a long snooze... until the hare fell fast into a proper sleep. Meanwhile the tortoise plodded steadily on until he passed the deep-dreaming hare. None of the general population had disturbed him. The tortoise was almost at the finishing post when the hare woke up and shook his thoughts into some sort of order. He remembered he was supposed to be winning something. A RACE?

BUT IT WAS TOO LATE...

…As the hare came speeding up to the finishing post THE TORTOISE CROSSED THE LINE **AND WON.**

The hare was thoroughly humiliated. For a long time afterwards the general population made snoring noises whenever the hare was in earshot or glanced into the distance to shout "TORTOISE COMING!" None of this did much to slow the hare down, but he was at least less annoying, and there was still a good chance that someday he would end up testing the hardness of a tree trunk, or the firmness of the ground at the end of a long drop or, of course, the sharpness of a crocodile's teeth…

not flying but falling

IN WHICH A TORTOISE IGNORES EXPERT ADVICE

# THERE WAS ONCE A TORTOISE

whose head was always in the clouds, though the rest of him all too firmly hugged the earth. THE TORTOISE DREAMED, as no other tortoise had dreamed, OF FLYING.

Swallows scooted low across the grassland, rich blue darts of squealing, aggravating speed, each flit and turn filling the tortoise with envy. Butterflies flapped like damp handkerchiefs in the shimmering heat of the afternoon. Even the earthbound ants grew wings and flew. IT WAS UNFAIR.

Dragonflies rattled and reversed over pools, and damselflies, bright turquoise hyphens, hovered among the bulrushes.

Bats flew and fished the evening skies, airy mice on shivering parchment wings. Even seeds from brainless, thoughtless rooted plants were lifted into aimless flight on the slightest breeze. Every flying thing conspired to make the tortoise angry, unfairly treated by nature, so wingless, so solid, so very keen to leave the ground.

He wanted just for once to look down on the earth and to enjoy the vast freedom of the high thin air where the eagle circled, master of the sky. So it was to the eagle that the tortoise went. He asked the eagle ever so politely for lessons in the glorious art of flying. The eagle did not laugh at this.

"When you grow wings, my little pebble," he said. "You are as solid as the earth you walk upon." But the tortoise still insisted he was born to fly. "Close cousin of a rock," said the eagle, "you are as airworthy as a stone." And he added not unkindly, "You are a tortoise and therefore aerodynamically suited to a slow life on the ground."
The tortoise was not deterred. "All I need is a little help. Once I'm free of the earth I can flap my legs."

After months of relentless pestering the tortoise, so thoroughly convinced of his flying ability and so desperate for a chance, touched the eagle's heart. If determination could keep a creature airborne, this one might yet fly.

And so the eagle took the tortoise up
into the high thin air where his dreams had always flown,
and there the eagle launched him into the clear sky and
left him to the whim of GRAVITY AND THE WIND...

ELEVEN

# fool's gold

IN WHICH
A FARMER **LOSES**
HIS GOLDEN GOOSE

# THERE WAS ONCE A GOOSE

WHO LAID, by strange and unlucky chance, ONE GOLDEN EGG EACH DAY. Her owner considered himself very fortunate, as this curious quirk of nature had steadily helped him to become a wealthy man. He no longer needed to work. His life became one of ease and comfort, and each day his faithful goose laid another golden egg.

He had everything he needed and nothing to think about but what he might buy next. As his desires became ever more extravagant, he suggested to his goose that she lay her golden eggs a little faster. There always seemed to be more things he wanted than he had money to buy. He became impatient.

"Goose," he asked tersely, "perhaps you could try laying another egg each day. Two eggs would be nice!" But she was no more capable of changing her habits than any other goose.

"Three eggs a day?" he continued. "Yes, three would be enough… or four. Four is a nice even number, not too much to ask…

But five, five is a handful, yes, maybe a handful a day... although
six is a more usual number... for eggs. Half a dozen golden eggs would
make me so happy...” And so he became a greedy man. “Seven ...
maybe eight, or nine. Nine is such a lovely number... three times three,
very lucky... but then ten is so much easier... two handfuls... good for
making calculations...,” he said, calculating in his busy mind,
“or eleven... maybe not eleven, neither one thing nor another... twelve,
now there's a thought. Twelve! A lovely round dozen golden eggs each
day... or a baker's dozen... thirteen, but thirteen is unlucky... add
one more... fourteen, a handsome number but maybe not quite as good
as fifteen...

TWENTY... THIRTY... FIFTY...

no, not good enough!”

He could not wait. He did not want to be counting eggs forever. No,
he wanted every golden egg he was due NOW. No more waiting for the
goose to lay, no more waiting to buy what he wanted to buy. It would be
so much better to get all this out of the way so he could enjoy a life of
ease, spending more and thinking less.

So he killed the goose for her golden eggs. But inside there was no hoard
of treasure, no instant fortune, not even one single small golden egg
more. With no goose there would be nothing... every day... forever...
nothing but hard work and sour regret.

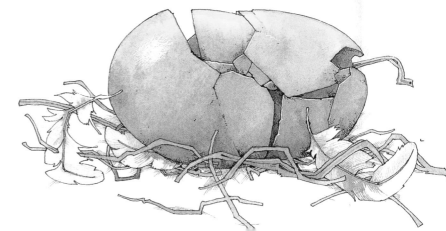

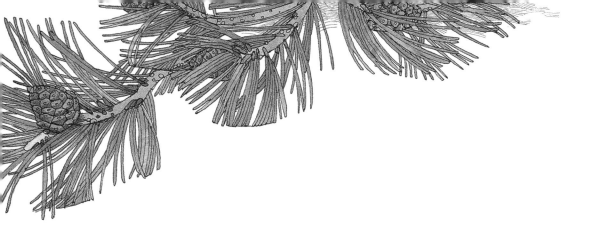

hard cheese

TWELVE

IN WHICH A FOX PERSUADES

A CROW OUT OF HIS LUNCH

# THERE WAS ONCE A CROW

sitting in a tree, holding a large, fresh cheese in his beak and feeling very pleased with himself. In fact, he was so pleased that he was just sitting there on his branch enjoying the all-round sense of well-being and smugness that the cheese was giving him WHEN A FOX WANDERED INTO THE STORY...

... A story that had begun when a freshly made cheese was left too close to an open window and the crow had stolen it. And would end, thought the fox confidently, with the cheese safely in his mouth. Another opportunity for trickery, thought the fox (and lunch)!

So the fox sat under the tree and looked up at the crow until at last the crow looked uneasily down at the fox.

"I was just admiring your particularly fine feathers," said the fox. "Have you discovered some new birdbath on your travels?  Your eyes seem particularly bright too, and as for your toes... so dark and shiny... and your beak gleaming in the sunlight...

so perfectly set off by the creamy whiteness of whatever that is you have a hold of. Quite magnificent!" The crow was becoming more astonished and pleased with himself by the moment.

"And," continued the fox, "a little bird was saying only this morning that you're not just a pretty face. I was told that you can sing beautifully too. In fact, I understand you have the most remarkable singing voice for miles around... that you can move your audience from tears to laughter with a single note... that the nightingales hereabouts have all retired early..." Here the fox thought he had better stop, only adding, "How I would love to hear that melifluous voice of yours. It would be such a privilege. A private performance — a mere verse or two?..."

THE CROW, SO OVERWHELMED WITH FLATTERY, felt a helpless urge to sing. He opened his beak... "CAW... CAW!" he went, unsweetly and tunelessly as only a crow can.

At the first note the cheese fell, bouncing from branch to branch to plummet into the fox's wide open, waiting jaws. And that's where the story, as the fox predicted, ends.

helen war

# THERE WAS ONCE A LITTLE GIRL

who liked to draw and paint and make things, sometimes out of paper or fabric and sometimes out of mud, sticks and grass-clippings. She climbed trees and never fell out. She read lots of books and listened to what everyone told her, but she did not say much because she was very shy.

She wanted to be an illustrator and her parents, who were (and still are) artists, thought that this was a good idea. So, in a September gale, she went to the seaside where there was an art college to learn all about it. After three years she left and started to illustrate books for children. She had learned a little bit about her job but she kept learning and she thinks, if she keeps trying, that one day she might know enough to be good at it.

**10** Write down any other markings (such as staccato, slurs, accents etc.) and their meanings:

**11** How would you describe the character or mood of the piece? Does it change?

**12** How will you communicate this in your performance?

**13** Find out something interesting about the composer:

**14** Find out the names of some other pieces by the composer:

**15** Are there any particular rhythms or repeated rhythmic patterns in the piece? Write them down here, and then clap them:

**16** Have you found anything tricky or challenging in the piece? Which bars will require special practice?

# Explore your piece

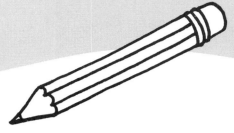

**1** Title

**2** Composer

**3** Period

*See page 24 for help*

**4** What does the title tell you about the music?

**5** What key is the piece in? Does it change? What is the relative key?

**6** Are there any scale or arpeggio patterns in the music?
Which scales or arpeggios are they? In which bars do they occur?

**7** Explain the time signature. Does it change?

**8** What will you count?

**9** Write down all the dynamics that occur
(including *cresc.* and *dim.*). List them in order of soft – loud:

WITHOUT MUSIC

What key is the piece in? Improvise a short piece in this key.

Now say the names of the notes of the scale and arpeggio up and down three times, then play them. What is the relative key? What is the key beginning on the dominant note? Now play those scales and arpeggios!

WITHOUT MUSIC

Choose a dynamic level or articulation marking from section 9 or 10 of *Explore your piece*, and make up a short piece concentrating on it. Think of a title before you begin.

Try to remember the piece (perhaps writing it down so that you can practise it again).

WITHOUT MUSIC

Think about the title. What does it tell you about the character of the piece?

Now make up your own short and simple piece with the same character, for either hand. Think carefully about that character, then compose another piece with the opposite character.

WITHOUT MUSIC

What is the time signature of the piece?

Make up a simple rhythm (four to eight bars in length) in this time signature. Write your rhythm down.

Now improvise a tune to fit the rhythm.

WITHOUT MUSIC

Play as much of the piece as you can from memory, including the dynamics, phrasing, and other markings. Play it with character and expression.

WITHOUT MUSIC

Choose a scale you are currently learning and play it beginning and ending with the top note.

Now practise it descending $p$ and ascending $f$.

WITHOUT MUSIC

Find another piece (perhaps from your sight-reading book) that is in the same key or uses some of the same patterns as your piece. Study it silently, hearing it in your head and imagining your fingers on the keys. Practise any tricky bits and finally, feeling a strong, steady pulse, play it slowly and as accurately as possible.

WITHOUT MUSIC

Practise the scale and arpeggio of the piece slowly, with even rhythm and tone. Then combine playing the scale and arpeggio with one ingredient from *Explore your piece*.

Now make up a short piece in $\frac{4}{4}$ using the scale and arpeggio patterns you've been working on.

WITHOUT MUSIC

What colour (or colours) does the piece make you think of? Improvise a short piece that conjures up that colour!

WITHOUT MUSIC

Choose one of the rhythms from section 15 of *Explore your piece* and practise the scale of the piece using that rhythm.

WITHOUT MUSIC

Play the keynote of the piece.

Working out the notes in your head first, now try to sing the 3rd, then the 5th note of the scale. Afterwards, check them by playing the notes on the piano.

WITHOUT MUSIC

Close your eyes and play a note on the piano. Try to guess the note. Repeat this a few times.

WITH MUSIC

Choose a bar from section 16 of *Explore your piece*. Think about the problem carefully and then compose two or three short exercises to help you practise it: for example, by repeating a particular finger movement, playing it at different speeds, or changing the rhythm. Write the exercises down if you like.

WITH MUSIC

Play the piece (or part of it) through with no expression at all.

Now play the same music with as much expression as you can, thinking about how to shape the phrases.

WITH MUSIC

Choose a short passage and then play it:

- *ff*
- *pp*
- with a *crescendo* and *diminuendo*
- much slower than marked
- at the correct tempo
- from memory

WITH MUSIC

Practise the first eight bars, beginning from bar two. Then do the same, this time beginning from bar three.

WITH MUSIC

Reading the music, hear the piece through in your head. Remember to hear the dynamics and other markings too. Make sure you know the meanings of all the markings in the piece. Now try to hear the piece in your head again – this time from memory! Imagine yourself playing it with lots of expression.

WITH MUSIC

Choose a short passage (one or two bars). Play it, listening very carefully to the melodic shape.

Now play it starting one tone lower (either hand or hands together). Now sing the same passage at any comfortable pitch.

WITH MUSIC

Can you spot any repeated patterns in the piece? They may be rhythmic or melodic; exact or slightly altered each time.

Choose one pattern and use it to compose a short piece of your own.

WITH MUSIC

Tap the rhythm of each hand separately, on the closed lid of the piano. Now tap both hands together.

Now sing the rhythm of one hand (to 'la' or 'zoom' etc.) and tap the rhythm of the other hand.

WITH MUSIC

Choose a few bars and play them backwards (i.e. from right to left).

WITH MUSIC

Choose as much, or as little, of the piece as you like (it may be the whole piece!). Prepare and then perform it, making sure you really communicate the character. Decide if anything could be improved and then perform it again. Think about how you might introduce the piece to an audience.

WITH MUSIC

Work at a phrase and then try to play it with your eyes closed. Listen very carefully to your playing. Is the music in four-bar or other length phrases?

WITH MUSIC

Practise a passage thinking about the character of the music. Are you successfully achieving that character? What would you like to make someone listening to your performance think or feel?

**10** Write down any other markings (such as staccato, slurs, accents etc.) and their meanings:

**11** How would you describe the character or mood of the piece? Does it change?

**12** How will you communicate this in your performance?

**13** Find out something interesting about the composer:

**14** Find out the names of some other pieces by the composer:

**15** Are there any particular rhythms or repeated rhythmic patterns in the piece? Write them down here, and then clap them:

**16** Have you found anything tricky or challenging in the piece? Which bars will require special practice?

# Explore your piece

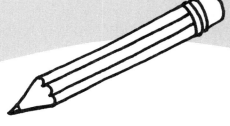

**1** Title

**2** Composer

**3** Period

*See page 24 for help*

**4** What does the title tell you about the music?

**5** What key is the piece in? Does it change? What is the relative key?

**6** Are there any scale or arpeggio patterns in the music? Which scales or arpeggios are they? In which bars do they occur?

**7** Explain the time signature. Does it change?

**8** What will you count?

**9** Write down all the dynamics that occur (including *cresc.* and *dim.*). List them in order of soft – loud:

14

**10** Write down any other markings (such as staccato, slurs, accents etc.) and their meanings:

**11** How would you describe the character or mood of the piece? Does it change?

**12** How will you communicate this in your performance?

**13** Find out something interesting about the composer:

**14** Find out the names of some other pieces by the composer:

**15** Are there any particular rhythms or repeated rhythmic patterns in the piece? Write them down here, and then clap them:

**16** Have you found anything tricky or challenging in the piece? Which bars will require special practice?

# Explore your piece

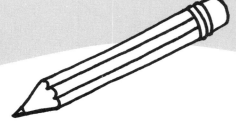

**1** Title

**2** Composer

**3** Period

*See page 24 for help*

**4** What does the title tell you about the music?

**5** What key is the piece in? Does it change? What is the relative key?

**6** Are there any scale or arpeggio patterns in the music?
Which scales or arpeggios are they? In which bars do they occur?

**7** Explain the time signature. Does it change?

**8** What will you count?

**9** Write down all the dynamics that occur
(including *cresc.* and *dim.*). List them in order of soft – loud:

**10** Write down any other markings (such as staccato, slurs, accents etc.) and their meanings:

**11** How would you describe the character or mood of the piece? Does it change?

**12** How will you communicate this in your performance?

**13** Find out something interesting about the composer:

**14** Find out the names of some other pieces by the composer:

**15** Are there any particular rhythms or repeated rhythmic patterns in the piece? Write them down here, and then clap them:

**16** Have you found anything tricky or challenging in the piece? Which bars will require special practice?

# Explore your piece

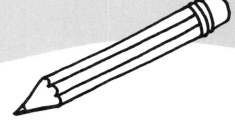

**1** Title

**2** Composer

**3** Period

*See page 24 for help*

**4** What does the title tell you about the music?

**5** What key is the piece in? Does it change? What is the relative key?

**6** Are there any scale or arpeggio patterns in the music?
Which scales or arpeggios are they? In which bars do they occur?

**7** Explain the time signature. Does it change?

**8** What will you count?

**9** Write down all the dynamics that occur
(including *cresc.* and *dim.*). List them in order of soft – loud:

**10** Write down any other markings (such as staccato, slurs, accents etc.) and their meanings:

**11** How would you describe the character or mood of the piece? Does it change?

**12** How will you communicate this in your performance?

**13** Find out something interesting about the composer:

**14** Find out the names of some other pieces by the composer:

**15** Are there any particular rhythms or repeated rhythmic patterns in the piece? Write them down here, and then clap them:

**16** Have you found anything tricky or challenging in the piece? Which bars will require special practice?

19

# Practice diary

As your practice develops each week, decide on one special feature.
It may, for example, be one of the following:

· part or all of one of your pieces that you can play really well
· a technical challenge that you've overcome
· an improvisation (one that you can remember!)
· a particular scale you can play really well
· your own composition

Write it down in the table below and show it to your teacher.
It will become a very good starting point for the next lesson.

| Week beginning | This week's special feature |
| --- | --- |
|  |  |
|  |  |
|  |  |
|  |  |
|  |  |
|  |  |
|  |  |
|  |  |
|  |  |
|  |  |
|  |  |
|  |  |
|  |  |
|  |  |

# Exam checklist

You may want to work through this section with your teacher.

*Scales, arpeggios and broken chords*
List all the scales etc. you need to know for the exam, or those that you are currently working on:

*Aural*
List the different tests you'll need to do:

## Countdown to an exam

Tick each statement as soon as you feel it to be true! Award yourself a treat when all are ticked.

### 3 weeks to go ...

◯ I can play all my scales slowly but accurately, rhythmically and with a good and even tone.

◯ I'm practising sight-reading every day.

◯ I know exactly what the aural tests require me to do and have had a lot of help with them.

◯ I can play my pieces fairly fluently and with expression.

### 2 weeks to go ...

◯ I can play all my scales slowly but accurately and fluently.

◯ I'm practising sight-reading every day.

◯ I've had a lot of practice at the aural tests.

◯ I can play my pieces fluently, with expression and character.

### 1 week to go ...

◯ I can play all my scales accurately, fluently and confidently.

◯ I'm still practising sight-reading every day.

◯ I'm confident about the aural tests.

◯ I've performed all my pieces to friends/relatives confidently and with lots of musical expression and character.

### 1 day to go ...

◯ I'm really looking forward to the exam and am going to get a good night's sleep!

# Useful stuff

Bear in mind that these dates are intended as a guide only.

| Composer dates | Period |
| --- | --- |
| c.1425–1600 | Renaissance |
| c.1600–1750 | Baroque |
| c.1750–1820 | CLASSICAL |
| c.1820–1915 | Romantic |
| c.1915–2000 | 20th Century |
| 2000 + | 21st Century |

## Notes

## Too tired to practise?

Then do one of the following activities instead:

1. Practise away from the piano – just sit down with the piece you're learning and hear it through in your head. Think particularly about the character.

2. Listen to some music – another piece by the same composer, a piece by another composer living at the same time, or some music in the same style. Your teacher will help.

3. Do a **PEP** analysis on the piece you are learning:
   **P** is for *problems* – decide what problems you still have to solve, technical or rhythmic for example. Make a note of them.
   **E** is for *expression* – what will you be trying to convey in your performance?
   **P** is for *practice* – the next practice! What in particular will you practise in your next session? Write your intentions down.